A Walk on the Wild Side

Carole Morland

HAYLOFT

First published 2008

Hayloft Publishing Ltd, South Stainmore, Kirkby Stephen, Cumbria, CA17 4DJ

tel: + 44 (0) 17683) 42300
fax. + 44 (0) 17683) 41568
e-mail: books@hayloft.eu
web: www.hayloft.eu

ISBN 1 904524 58 3

A catalogue record for this book is available from the British Library

Printed and bound in the EU

Papers used by Hayloft are natural, recyclable products made from wood grown in sustainable forests.
The manufacturing processes conform to the environmental regulations of the country of origin.

To Bert for sharing his knowledge and enthusiasm and

to Brian and Mark for being simply the best.

The author judging at the Australian Horse of the Year Show, Melbourne, 2008.
Photograph courtesy Dillwyn Moss (Australia)

CONTENTS

Lunesdale mares and foals on Roundthwaite Common.
Photograph courtesy of Kit Houghton.

INTRODUCTION

THE SEMI-FERAL Fell pony herds of Great Britain are becoming fewer, and to my knowledge there has not, so far, been written very much about the life-style and behaviour of such herds. This book therefore is an endeavour to record the behaviour and way of life of one such herd from my own observations over a long period of time.

I hope to show how the ponies communicate with each other, how hierarchy is achieved, respected and understood by the herd, and how they react to various situations, fears and challenges. Once we understand how the wild Fell pony thinks and communicates with its own kind, then we ourselves can enter into a better relationship with the domesticated Fell pony. By using signals that they immediately understand and accept and by understanding their natural fears and dislikes we may be able to establish an easier and quicker way of taming and training a Fell pony. Throughout the book therefore I shall be attempting to make comparisons with the way the ponies behave in the wild and in a domesticated situation.

I do not propose to go into the history of how the Fell pony, as we know it today arrived, as much has already been written on these lines. However, going back much further than before individual breeds emerged, the evolution process resulted in an herbivorous hoofed animal that belongs to a group of animals whose extremities support them uniquely on the ground, the last phalanx of the toe being covered with horn. All of the horse's weight is supported by the 'central toe' – a unique feature that has evolved over thousands of years and resulted in a hard hoof, and in the case of the Fell pony of a distinctive 'blue' horn. Coupled with strong limbs, powerful muscles, a complex skeleton and very well developed senses which alerted the animal to, and allowed it to flee from danger, the horse evolved and more importantly survived!

There are several different lines of thought as to how the distinctive breed that we now know as the Fell pony developed and I am not going to argue as to who may be right or wrong. Enough to say that the semi-feral herds of Fell ponies in Cumbria should be recognised as being as important to this area as the Dartmoor, Exmoor and New Forest ponies are to their native areas.

Roundthwaite Common, which is the home of the Lunesdale ponies, is crossed by bridlepaths, so it is not possible to run a stallion loose with the herd here. However we also have 'enclosed' fell land on which it is possible to run a stallion with mares, so my observations have been based upon both a 'true' herd, accompanied by a stallion and family groups consisting only of mares and daughters.

HIERARCHY

IN THEIR NATURAL state, horses and ponies have always been a common prey for animals such as wolves and pumas which thankfully no longer roam in England, but still continue to be predators in other countries. Having neither horns nor antlers, the defence mechanism, which has enabled equines to survive for thounsands of years, is the ability to run.

Contrary to popular belief, when a herd accompanied by a stallion, flees from danger, it is not the stallion which heads the herd, but the 'lead' mare. The stallion brings up the rear, thereby putting himself between the herd and the perceived 'danger.' In this position he can also herd along the 'stragglers,' which may be the older ponies that are no longer as swift or agile as the younger herd members.

There is a definite 'hierarchy' that governs the running of such a herd – each animal having a set place in the scheme of things from the highest placed, which is normally, but not always the stallion, to the lowest foal. Sometimes the leader may be a mare of great character. To be the herd leader does not mean that they must be the most aggressive, rather that they have demonstrated to the rest of the herd, their ability to impress and govern by courage, intelligence and confidence.

The difference between a totally feral or semi-feral herd leader, and the leader in a domesticated group, is that the position of leader in a domesticated group is often achieved through bullying or intimidation rather than courage, intelligence and earning the respect of the rest of the herd.

The responsibility for the safety of the herd lies with the leader, be it mare or stallion, and it is the leader that will decide the direction that the herd will take if fleeing from a possible source of danger. When a herd 'flees' from perceived danger, the foals follow their mothers without question and the basic rule is that the rest all follow and do not overtake a pony of a higher rank. If this occurs, they are 'punished' with a sharp nip, a method which is also used, by the herd leader in order to chastise youngsters who get out of line before they have learned all the herd 'rules' on a variety of different things.

This system of hierarchy is therefore both understood and accepted by each pony, and can be used to man's advantage when teaching a domesticated pony to lead. By not allowing the pony that we are leading to go past our shoulder; giving it a dig with our elbow if it does,

The ability to flee has ensured the survival of all equines. Photograph courtesy of Kit Houghton.

and by adopting a firm attitude, we are demonstrating leadership, which it will accept as a natural and well understood signal. When a pony is mounted by a rider, it is also accepting that the rider is the 'leader.'

The deciding of the highest placed in the hierarchy system between two stallions, in other words which should be herd leader, can involve violence.

This, put into a 'domesticated' situation was demonstrated to me quite forcefully when we bought back Lunesdale Henry, who we had sold some years previously. He had been running with a group of mares, some of which had been quite large, and he, being a traditional 13.2h.h. pony, had been unable to cover them. This had resulted in a certain amount of frustration, which had transformed him from being a pony of a quiet and reasonable nature into quite an aggressive pony.

This was demonstrated to us in no uncertain terms on the first day that he arrived back at our farm. He was let out into the yard whilst we 'mucked out' his loose box. When we went to catch him he literally went berserk. He refused to be caught and ran around the yard with ears laid back and charging (open mouthed and roaring) at anyone he saw. At one point he backed up to my car and delivered two hefty kicks which left two large dents in

It is a breathtaking sight when a herd of Fell ponies gallop down the fellside in unison. Photograph courtesy of Kit Houghton.

my car's rear which did not impress me greatly.

He then proceeded to jump over a wall into the adjacent paddock. The wall was about three feet high on the side from which he jumped, but the drop at the other side was nearer to five feet! He was completely undeterred by this and when we opened the gate back into the yard he once again entered the yard, snorting and roaring and running at anyone in sight. We had enough staff to try to surround him but in order to evade capture he ran into the cow byre. He found himself in the narrow gangway where the cows were fed and facing a solid wall. There was no way out unless he went backwards.

Bert, my husband, went in from the opposite end and faced him, armed with a piece of alkathene hose. Henry attacked, with mouth open and ears laid back and at the crucial moment Bert whacked him across the nose with the alkathene hose. Henry attacked several more times and a neighbour and friend, Bill Potter, who was there at the time, said: 'If you miss him Bert, he will kill you.'

Bert did not miss and the battle raged for some time. Henry then gave the sign of submission. He recognised Bert as being the herd leader and Bert recognised Henry's sign of submission and approached him and placed a halter on him and 'backed' him out of the gangway. From that day onwards Henry was, (and still is at the time of writing this), at the age of 29-years-old, the perfect gentleman. He was from that day onwards a happy pony, knowing his position with regard to humans and both giving and receiving respect. However, from this leadership battle evolved a funny story…

One of the people present that day who witnessed Henry's temporary loss of sanity was a young man who had helped Bert with the horses and on the farm in previous years, and who happened to be visiting that particular day. Bert asked him to stand between the wall and the cattle lorry and if Henry should attempt to go between the two, it was this young man's job to stop him. Henry charged between lorry and wall and headed for the young man with ears laid back, nostrils flaring and mouth open. Our man did not pause for long – he turned tail and ran for cover!

When all the excitement had subsided and Henry had given up his position as 'herd leader' we had a phone call from another friend who was coming to pick up a sheep dog that he had bought, and who also was close friends with the young man in question. Bert told him what had happened with Henry and persuaded this friend to tell the young man that he had purchased a little black Fell stallion, called Henry, from Bert and to ask his help in collecting this stallion. Our friend managed to do this with a straight face. The young man then told our friend in no uncertain terms that 'no way was he coming to help him collect that bloody stallion' and he also added for good measure, ' if you have any sense at all you will call off the deal!'

The stallion and the highest ranked mare in a wild herd do not quarrel but live in harmony, each playing their respective roles.

Hierarchy also governs which animals are first to drink at the watering 'hole' and which are the first to roll in either a dry or a boggy area of the fell designated for this purpose. The lower ranking animals accept this, mostly without quarrel, as on the plus side, they receive protection from the older and more experienced members of the herd. Even when drinking, the herd leader will raise his or her head in between drinks to look out for, listen for and sniff the air for, possible danger, and for this same reason the herd will choose to rest in strategic places where this vigilance is best carried out. The older members of the herd will know and teach the younger members where the best places are on the fells to find shelter in harsh weather, the best grazing at various times of the year and the dangerous places to avoid.

This social hierarchy and dominance is not achieved in the same way as in domesticated groups. Every foal learns from birth the position that it holds within the herd and this is not questioned and no animal born into the herd is subjected to bullying. This is completely different to groups of domesticated ponies where dominance may have been achieved through bullying and where it can be dangerous to introduce a new and possibly younger member without first placing them in an adjacent field for a time. To 'introduce' without

Lunesdale Henry, after losing his battle for leadership with Bert Morland, becomes a perfect gentleman for the rest of his life.

preparation, a young pony, especially a colt, into an already established domestic group can cause it to be subjected to extremes of humiliation.

Social rank may in some cases be inherited rather than earned. The daughters of a higher ranked mare will automatically achieve a higher rank in the herd than the daughters of mares that are ranked lower. Family ties are strong, memory is exceptional, and ranks are not forgotten. This was proved to us when Lunesdale Rebecca was returned to Roundthwaite Common after an absence of three years when on loan down south. We observed (from a discrete distance on the quad bike) the fact that she bypassed several groups of ponies until she found the group consisting of her mother and sisters. She was not only immediately accepted back into the group, but also claimed her rightful rank as second to her mother, seeing as she was the eldest daughter in the group. This situation was accepted without argument by her younger sisters, even though they had never left the group.

In a semi-feral herd, such as the Lunesdale ponies, some human interference takes place that can alter the scheme of things and therefore the hierarchy amongst the young stock that would normally exist if the ponies were left completely untouched. For instance, the foals are weaned and wintered inside and only the fillies are

Leader mare Lunesdale White Rose. Photograph courtesy of Real Time Imaging.

*Leader mare Lunesdale White Rose giving the signal to
the group to 'flee'.*

re-introduced to the fell in the spring when they will rejoin their family group.

If a herd was left completely untouched, it is likely that both colts and fillies would remain with the herd until two years of age (as still happens within certain wild herds in other countries), when the colts would be 'sent packing' to join up with other bachelors. These bachelors would roam together until maturity at about six years of age when they would either mate with young fillies who had left the herd of their birth, thereby forming 'harems' of their own or would challenge an older male for the right to take over his herd.

As the fillies approach two years of age in a 'managed' herd, such as the Lunesdales, they are removed. At three years of age they are either mated with a stallion of different bloodlines and then returned to their family group on the open fell or in some cases added to the harem of the stallion running on the 'enclosed' fell. However, fillies left in a completely wild and unmanaged herd would normally wander off at this age in search of a mate and would not normally mate with their sire. Ensuring that they do not mate until three years of age is another way that we help the fillies to maintain fitness and growth.

TIES AND FRIENDSHIPS

THE TIES THAT bind semi-feral ponies are threefold: those of family, friendship and leadership.

Family ties are strong, especially between female groups that live a semi-feral existence without a stallion and that consist of matriarch, daughters, grand-daughters, and other females. These can last for many years and can withstand separation for several years proving that these ponies also have good memories and powers of recognition. The matriarch will often assume the role of a stallion and herd protector, looking out for her daughters and grand-daughters and leading the group away from perceived danger. We have watched Lunesdale White Rose, after having been brought down from the fell and put in a field with the rest of the in-foal mares. She has patrolled back and forth, showing a belligerent expression to, and putting herself between, other non-related mares and her daughter, Lunesdale Rebecca, who had just recently foaled.

Friendships are formed (as are dislikes) in much the same way as humans between all age groups from foals to adults. Foals will play and mutually groom some of their contemporaries whilst ignoring others, as will

Establishing the hierarchy between young colts can involve a certain amount of fighting.

adults. Mares that dislike each other will co-exist in the same herd but will keep their distance and not enter into play or mutual grooming. Mares who are friends will play together on occasions, graze together, groom each other and allow one another to put their heads under the other's tail to rid their faces of flies.

Friendships are also formed between young bachelors of two-years-old and upwards that are cast out of 'true' wild herds. Because they are such social animals, in the 'true' wild, an aged stallion that has been successfully challenged for the right to take over his herd by a younger stallion, will happily live with a group of young bachelors rather than live alone. There are recorded cases of aged wild stallions in some countries that have formed relationships with other animals such as antelopes rather than remain alone. This also affirms why it is possible to turn out young colts together in captivity that have not had sexual contact with a female. They will exist quite happily together after first establishing their own hierarchy. It also explains why some domesticated horses and ponies that are kept alone, form strong ties with other domestic animals such as goats or dogs.

Within a herd that has a stallion running with it, the stallion will have strong ties of friendship with some of the mares, other than just during the mating season and

will search them out for companionship and mutual grooming.

Likewise a stallion can often be observed playing gently with foals of both sexes. Perhaps this recognition of younger and weaker animals is why it has been observed that both wild and domesticated ponies may often allow small children to take greater liberties with them, without coming to harm, than they would adults! Although I personally have not witnessed it (as not many children climb up our fells) I have heard of wild horses in other countries approaching groups of playing children with no malicious intent whatsoever: merely to observe them at close quarters in an entirely benign way!

The third tie, is probably the most important in semi-feral or feral herds and is that of leadership as the strongest of all instincts in any animal is probably that of survival, and the survival of the herd is usually perceived to be the responsibility of the herd leader. Once leadership is recognised, the rest of the herd will respect and obey the leader's instructions without question.

A group of colts indulge in some mutual grooming.

Once the hierarchy has been established a group of two-year-old colts live together amicably.

Rituals

THERE ARE MANY 'rituals' that are observed within a wild herd that may either differ or cease to exist entirely between domesticated Fell ponies. Of these the main ones are of courtship and mating, introduction, defecation and challenge between stallions.

One of the most regularly observed rituals is that of courtship and mating. In the wild, a Fell stallion will perform a courtship ritual that will take considerably longer than the actual act of mating. In addition to the usual approach of scenting the mare's urine, baring the teeth in an almost 'comical' grin and sniffing the air, the stallion in the wild will also perform a kind of courtship 'dance' which is rarely seen with stallions covering 'in hand' or in domesticated circumstances.

With his tail lifted, his neck arched and his nose facing inwards to the mare, he will perform a series of steps in front of the mare to finally impress her. If the required receptive signals are received the mating will go ahead, but if they are not, the process will be repeated. Ponies that have been brought up amongst others, and especially in a natural environment, will have learned from birth how to interpret equine body language.

Occasionally a colt that has been reared in a solitary domestic environment will not be able to mate with a mare, as he has not learned how to interpret the signals that will show whether she is receptive or not to mating and he may be intimidated by her reactions. He is also more likely to be injured by the mare than a colt that can correctly interpret the mare's body language.

Sometimes a mare can be attacked and injured when turned into an already established herd which has a stallion running with it. This can happen for a variety of reasons. The mare may have been brought up as a solitary animal and may not be able to read the signals or obey the necessary rituals. She may have been 'teased' or 'tried' as to whether she is in season and may have the scent of another male on her or the stallion may merely take a dislike to her.

We have seen this to be the case when a stallion will just refuse to have anything to do with a mare introduced to the herd even though she is obviously in season. We have also had other mares brought to one of our stallions that have shown quite severe bite marks inflicted by another stallion, that either took a dislike to her and therefore refused to cover her, or found it impossible to cover her because she was too fat. It is better therefore to 'err on the side of caution' and cover visiting mares in hand rather than introduce them to an established herd if the stallion in question has shown aggressive tendencies to 'outside' mares. Equally a stallion may show preferences and if one or more of his own 'herd' mares are in season will cover them at frequent intervals but refuse to cover a visiting mare even though she is also in season. On occasions, a dominant mare will try to prevent the stallion from mating with other mares. In the case of a young and inexperienced stallion, the mare may actually succeed, but an older, more experienced stallion may retaliate, resulting in injury to the mare.

Another ritual, which is also frequently observed amongst domesticated ponies, is that of mutual grooming. The ponies will firstly approach each other with mouths semi-open and ears back in a submissive position. If mutual confidence is established then they will proceed to groom each other by scraping each other's skin with their teeth. This is obviously enjoyed by both parties as the ears are always in the 'relaxed' position. It is also a way to rid the coat of itches and parasites. Foals also observe this ritual from a very early age. On some occasions domesticated animals will attempt to reciprocate this with their owners, and it is a great way to establish friendship if you are not too fussy about your clothes being grated by equine teeth!

A strict ritual or code is observed within the wild herd about the area of ground that may be used for defecation. Mares will defecate in an area that is not used for grazing. Stallions will carry this a step further and not only will not defecate in an area that is used for grazing but will position themselves so that the faeces are dropped in a single neat and high pile. This behaviour can be observed to a certain extent in domesticated ponies. Owners who keep stallions in a stable will notice that the excrement is usually in a certain part of the loose box in a neat pile. Fell ponies that are kept in too small an area that does not allow them a separate area in which to defecate will eventually become unhappy and lose condition. This situation is generally described as the pasture having become 'horse sick'.

A further ritual observed by wild ponies is that of not all grazing at the same time. One or more of them is usually on 'sentry' duty, ready to alert the herd to any perceived danger. This is seldom seen in a domestic herd where all ponies can often be seen grazing at the same time.

Probably the most menacing and somewhat strange ritual between wild ponies is that which is observed when two stallions challenge each other. When such a challenge takes place each stallion tenses his muscles and with his head and tail in the erect position snorts loudly and menacingly. They each move around in a circle taking turns to deposit a small amount of excrement on the same pile. If one stallion submits, then the other deposits the final amount of excrement and the whole thing comes to a halt. If however neither animal submits, the ensuing battle can be ferocious and the resulting injuries, which are usually bites to the neck, broken jaws and skinned knees can result in death.

Even at this early age the colts are mindful of the serious side of life as it can be quite clearly observed that one colt is on 'sentry' duty while the others graze.

In a 'managed' herd such as the Lunesdale, the situation would not arise whereby a young stallion challenged an older stallion for the right to take over the herd. There has only been the odd occasion, thankfully, when a stallion has broken out of his quarters and challenged another. The situation was resolved with a lot of shouting and a broom handle before any serious injury could be inflicted. Contrary to popular belief, battles between stallions in true wild herds are not frequent and challenges are more often than not resolved by one of the stallions giving the sign of submission. This 'ritual' preceding a challenge between stallions is not observed when, for instance, two stallions get loose at a show where neither one is on its 'home territory'. In these cases it is usually an instant attack.

COMMUNICATION

LIKE THE SOCIAL animals that they are, Fell ponies possess a large range of ways of communicating with each other and with man. In the 'wild' state, these signals which can be either vocal or body language, are finely honed and without them they would not be able to live as a herd. These methods of communication are learned from birth and ponies that have been bought as foals and reared in a solitary state may not be able to either recognise them at all, or will only be able to interpret them in a 'loose' way.

The vocal ways of communication in a wild herd are by whinnies, snorts, squeals, bellows, groans and murmurs:

Whinnies are emitted as a sign of greeting or recognition and it appears that ponies in a wild herd recognise the whinnies of other herd members. The whinny is used to advertise a pony's presence and by a mare calling for her foal. The last type of whinny is more delicate and sweet. The whinny made by a domesticated pony to a human bringing food is a deeper and friendlier tone than that exchanged between two herd members. Another deep and more prolonged whinny is that made by a stallion during courtship.

Snorts indicate nervous excitement, most likely because a perceived danger exists, or when they encounter something strange and unrecognised, and to which they wish to draw the attention of the herd, or when they wish to issue a challenge to another pony.

Squeals are high pitched and can signify provocation, excitement, indignation or fear. Frequently the mares 'squeal' at the stallion during courtship.

Bellows or roars can be spine chilling and are emitted during emotional 'madness' or intense terror; normally during combat, or on occasions when a pony has been attacked, is being captured or cornered and has decided, rightly or wrongly, that it is a life or death situation!

Groans can probably be termed as being more than signals; being emitted when the animal is beyond the point of making other signals on occasions when they are subject to continuous effort such as during a prolonged birth or suffering from serious illness. Groans (of protest) of a lesser degree in domesticated ponies, can be heard when the pony is being mounted by a rider or getting up with difficulty in a confined space within, for example, a stable.

A **murmur,** which is a soft sort of 'bumpf' noise, reflects a state of fullness and satisfaction. It is a calmer and softer sound than a groan. Although it is heard amongst the wild mares when they have eaten their fill and the foal is suckling, it can more often be recognised in the domesticated pony on being happy to see its owner or when it is just plainly contented!

In addition to the vocal signs described above, there is a wide range of body signals that can be used to express the emotional state of an individual or to provoke and receive a response from another herd member. These methods of communication are learned from birth and thus can make the introduction to the herd of a 'bought in' pony that has been reared in a solitary manner very difficult. This is one of the reasons why we have, over the years, when buying in new brood mares, usually bought from other semi-feral herds of ponies. The other reason of course is that a mare that has lived a comparative 'life of ease' on a lowland farm or stud, would find it hard to maintain condition on the high fells.

The most basic meaning of body language is through the 'cast' of the pony's body. When it is calm and relaxed, it presents a gentle and unpronounced body outline, but when it is excited or alarmed, the muscles are tensed, the body is extended to maximum height and movements are elevated and abrupt. The two opposite ends of the scale are when for example the pony is sleeping, when the thigh joint is immobilised so one hip can be rested; head and tail are lowered and ears are dropped. At the other end of the scale, when the pony is on high alert, being excited or nervous, and in the case of a herd leader wishing to communicate this to the rest of the herd, there is a totally different body language. The outline is rigid, with muscles tensed, ears up, head and tail lifted and neck arched.

The way that a pony moves its neck is very significant. When the herd leader intends to gather members of the herd, the head is lowered and moved like a snake, 'dancing' from one side to the other and lifting a fore leg at the same time. It is the command to, 'Get moving' or in another case, tells a mare of a stallion's sexual intentions.

Another neck movement is when the neck is 'twisted.' This position is seen when they are playing or more seriously when they are showing hostile intentions of a malicious nature and on rare occasions when they have become so upset that they have lost touch with reality and become out of control or 'mad' for a few moments. I have only ever witnessed the latter on two occasions. The first was with Lunesdale Henry, which I have already described, and the second was with a bought in stallion who was stabled and who could smell another stallion in the vicinity. He savagely bit and rattled the bolts on his stable door and turned at intervals to actually bite his own body! He had truly become 'mad' for a while and was completely past the stage of reasoning.

In his defence, most of his problems had been 'man made' and he eventually became calmer and manageable. This was not achieved in the same way as with Lunesdale Henry. Having been reared in a 'solitary' state, he was not able to interpret the herd signals as a semi-feral pony and he thus responded to a mixture of firm handling, kindness and being kept well out of scenting distance of other stallions!

The way that a wild pony walks can tell the observer much about its mood and this is also true of domesticated ponies. One that walks with a light and bright step is content, excited or showing interest in its surroundings whilst one walking with a weary step is either disinterested or lazy. These ways of walking are usually accentuated by the carriage of the tail, that is carried high in the first instance and low in the second.

Lifting of the forelegs and 'pawing' the ground is usually a way of exploring an object. In the case of semi-feral ponies it can be a means of 'scratching' away the grass in order to get at the soil for additional salt or minerals or merely to 'scratch' the tongue against the soil which they seemingly find quite pleasurable. If the pawing is continuous and is not for the purpose of getting to the minerals or salt, then it can indicate frustration, disgust or sometimes, especially in the case of the domesticated animal, that it cannot get what it wants!

On the other hand to lift a foreleg to another pony can be a way of greeting or to indicate superiority and warn another pony not to come too close!

The position and movement of the tail also has great significance. As a general rule it can be assumed that the higher the tail, the greater the excitement and agitation of the pony and the lower the tail the greater the state of calm or in some cases submission. In the case of excessive submission, bordering on terror, the tail can be held between the legs. I have fairly recently witnessed this 'clamping' of the tail between the legs when judging a ridden show class and shortly after I witnessed the pony doing this, it exited the ring with great speed and determination. It was obviously greatly upset or fearful of something, but unfortunately the rider was not in the position to see it and thus be warned of the pony's intention!

Considerable tail 'whisking' movements are normal when a pony is getting rid of flies, but this whisking can also be observed when there is a problem such as boredom, anger, feeling ill or irritated. It can also be used in the case of the domesticated pony to express displeasure when being mounted or following instructions being given by a trainer that it does not enjoy!

There are also many movements of the head, ears and mouth that are used to give signals to other members of the herd. Ponies continually move their heads in order to rid themselves of flies but more importantly they move it up and down and from side to side in order to get the maximum field of vision. There are also movements that may be the result of an emotional or mental disorder, mostly in the case of the domesticated animal. In these cases the head may be pulled back and may signify a desire to escape or to show frustration or rejection. Mostly, when the head is 'pulled in' towards the body, it means that the pony wishes to leave the situation in which it finds itself and it is possible that it may follow this with rearing up.

A wild pony will signal an intended attack with its head lifted, the muzzle will go down quickly, and the ears will be laid flat; a sure sign of intended aggression.

Continual movement of the ears can be observed in most ponies, but more significantly in wild ponies. Sometimes the ears will be moved in different directions when the pony is giving attention to more than one sound. In general ears forward means either a state of alertness, alarm or friendly interest. When ponies are resting or sleeping, the ears are laid slightly towards the side and without signs of tension. Ears laid back can signify timidity or submission or in the case of two ponies grooming each other, relaxation. Ears laid flat against the head indicate fury or terror and they are in this position when a pony prepares to charge or kick an adversary.

The mouth can also be an indicator of feelings or mood; a relaxed mouth with no wrinkles can indicate a placid mood and when sleeping the pony may droop its lower lip. The most evident mouth signal is when a pony approaches another with its mouth wide open; a sure signal that it intends to bite. Approaching another pony with mouth half open is usually a means of 'testing' if the other is friendly and if both parties are satisfied that this is the case, then mutual grooming may follow.

Approaching with teeth bared is normally more of an intention to intimidate rather than actually bite. This showing of teeth in foals however is not a sign of intimidation but of submission in the face of older ponies and is usually accompanied by 'chattering' and an outstretched neck.

When a domesticated pony sticks out its tongue, it is usually a sign of discomfort in the pony's mouth, but ponies in the wild, especially young ponies, may do this as a sign of insecurity or hesitation.

Each position of the pony's body and muscles, tail, ears, and mouth therefore can indicate a mood or emotion and by better understanding of this 'body language' by which the semi-feral ponies communicate with each other, we can also achieve better communication with them.

HABITS, MOVEMENTS AND MEMORY

WILD FELL PONIES pass the main part of the day eating, wandering over a wide area to do so. Their diet consists of a wide range of grasses, herbs and roots and also when available certain fruits, leaves and occasionally tree bark, all of which have a positive influence on their health and strength. It is interesting to note that nowadays garlic plays an important part in the diet of many horses that are stabled and 'in training' for various disciplines, but wild garlic has always been available to these wild Fell ponies.

I am sure that there are many other natural 'cures' and 'additives' obtained from the herbage that is freely available on their native habitat. The only thing that the semi-feral ponies on Roundthwaite Common seem to lack is copper. This soil seems to have a copper deficiency that sometimes results in the coats of the black ponies having a brownish tinge. This is easily rectified for show purposes by feeding a copper supplement.

As I have already said they roam over a wide area when grazing and living in the wild. Consider then, the massive trauma that we are subjecting these ponies to when we start to domesticate them! By putting them in a stable or loose box, we are taking away their most basic instinct, that is the ability to flee from danger! Additionally we are making them dependant upon us to supply food and water, rather than them being able to find their own supplies.

In order to make this change as easy as possible on the pony, we need to make sure that the pony has adequate space and light, is able to 'look out' on the outside world and we need to make them feel that they can rely on us. This is best achieved by visiting, feeding, grooming, handling and turning out the pony at regular times of day. Like children, they seem to respond best to a routine, which they can rely on. Likewise we should also consider why many ponies immediately defecate when entering a trailer or horse box. It is their way of showing fear or nervousness. It is not in their nature to enter an enclosed space, let alone one that moves and they are not able to see out of!

When not eating or drinking, wild ponies rest, play and roll! Only at certain times of the year do they mate and give birth. Wild Fell mares will normally not start to come into season until spring and will not continue coming into season after late summer. This is nature's way of ensuring that the majority of foals are born when the grass supply is most plentiful in order for the mares to produce sufficient milk and so that the foals are not subject to the coldest of weather. Ovulation is stimulated by daylight and therefore in countries like England will normally take place between April and September. It has also been noted that when semen for artificial insemination purposes has been taken from Fell pony stallions, the quality of this semen is better during the months when natural mating in the wild would normally take place.

The areas that they choose to rest in will have good vantage points from where perceived danger can be best observed and certain, either dry and dusty or wet and muddy, places will be favourite 'rolling' places. In herds that have a stallion running with them, the stallion will be the first and the last to roll, thereby impregnating the place with his scent. The rest will roll in the order that the hierarchy allows.

A wild pony will normally only leave the herd for specific reasons. Firstly, in the case of a mare to give birth. She will leave the herd when foaling is imminent and will normally choose a damp place beside a ditch, marsh, pool or stream. The chosen place will also probably be on a bank or raised point that gives the best possible views of any approaching danger. Even though we bring the mares into the 'in fields' to foal, this instinct remains strong. We have, on a couple of occasions, had a foal drown immediately after birth when the mare has chosen a situation that was on a steep bank too near to a stream or river.

Wild ponies normally give birth just before dawn although there are exceptions. The birth process is usually quick, and wild Fell ponies seem to have a knack of hanging on to the foal until they are sure that they have privacy, when the foal will be on the ground within minutes. We had one occasion when a neighbour drove past one of our mares on his tractor quite late at night. She

A Fell pony mare stands guard over her resting foal.

was peacefully grazing with no obvious signs of an imminent birth and when he returned ten minutes later she had not only given birth but the foal was already trying to struggle to its feet.

An older pony will leave the herd in order to die, seemingly preferring to die alone and curiously enough they will choose exactly the same type of damp place as the mares choose to give birth in!

If no human interference occurs, there are only two other occasions when ponies will leave the herd of their own accord. Firstly, in the case of young fillies, to seek a stallion other than their father with which to mate and secondly, young colts to find fillies with which to set up their own 'harems.'

When the herd leader gives the signal to move 'en bloc' (for example to head to a place of shelter in bad weather), the herd will march in a determined order, following the leader. The way that ponies are able to focus their sight is by balancing the head: lowering, lifting and moving laterally and this can be observed when they are passing through difficult, narrow or dangerous places on the fell. This is when we should remember that a domesticated animal that is perhaps wearing blinkers and is held on a tight rein may feel unable to focus properly and may react in, what is to us, an unexpected way.

As the ability to run is the only defence mechanism

that these ponies possess, it is not surprising that they will avoid any element that they perceive may cause damage to their hooves or 'hold back' the feet in any way. For this reason they will avoid swampy areas and patches of loose sharp stones. They will also avoid treading in pools and in strong currents of water. It is this same reason that may make a domesticated Fell pony reluctant to cross either a river or a 'hollow' sounding bridge and to avoid shadows, drains and painted areas on roads.

The fact that a domesticated pony will enter a stream that is deep or has a fast flowing current, or will cross 'perceived' hazards on roads, or go across hollow sounding bridges, is a tribute to the driver or rider. It means that they have allowed their deep strong natural instinct to be over ridden by their trust in a human. It also means that we humans should not let this trust down!

If there is food and water in abundance it is rare for the family groups living on the fell to be territorial and various groups will cohabit in the same area quite happily. However, the leader mare will threaten a pony from another group that approaches too near to her offspring.

Wild Fell ponies have excellent memories and will avoid a place on the fell where an accident or death has occurred, even many years before. The morning after a night low flying exercise, carried out by the airforce we found a mare dead on some rocks at the foot of a steep slope of loose stones or shale. There were no outward signs of injury on her body except for a small hole, which had bled slightly, in her head. We were very concerned as to how she had met her death and therefore had a post mortem examination done on her body.

The vet who conducted this said that her internal injuries were consistent with having been hit by a heavy goods vehicle travelling at speed; including broken back, ribs and skull, and that death would have been instantaneous. We concluded that the low flying aircraft had startled her to the extent that she stepped on to the loose shale, something that she would not normally have done) from where she slid down the steep slope, gathering speed and crashing on to the rocks below. The other ponies now avoid this place quite noticeably.

Several other occurrences have emphasised to me their capability to remember places, people and voices. The first of these was 'orphan' Annie. Bert and I received a phone call while we were away at a market from a friend who had been checking on our sheep on the fell. He had come across a dead mare that had obvious signs of having been struck by lightning and her filly foal was standing alongside the mare's body. The foal was weak and did not struggle when he lifted it onto his knees and brought it back to the farm on the quad bike.

We discovered that it had grass in its mouth although it was not old enough to have started eating grass. We therefore surmised that it had been sucking the moisture from the wet grass in order to survive. We mixed dried milk and tried for several hours to get this foal to suck from a bottle with no success. Midnight was approaching, the foal was getting weaker, and I remembered reading somewhere that foals would sometimes drink from a bowl rather than suck from a bottle. I mixed one more feed, placed it in a bowl and Annie drank the lot! Four hourly feeds followed, and Bert rigged up a metal container that I was able to place a small household bucket into at a height that Annie could drink from.

The night shift was particularly exhausting and I was glad after a few weeks when I managed to get the last feed of the day at 11pm and the first at 6am. A further problem occurred when we realised that we had an overnight judging appointment. Luckily by this time, Annie had become a favourite with a couple of the neighbour's children and they undertook to do the feeding whilst I was away! Annie thrived and I tried to give her as normal a life as possible by taking her out into a small paddock each day. She thought this was great fun and would gallop round and round me in circles until it was time for bed when she would follow me back to her box.

However, despite my best efforts she was becoming too 'humanised.' This was brought home to me when I tried to leave her in the paddock on her own while I did a spot of gardening. Within minutes she had jumped a three foot high wall and was on the lawn alongside me. I had also not been able to get her to pull grass from the ground. She would eat it from my hand but would not pull it and eat it herself. I ignored Bert's suggestion that I should crawl around the paddock on all fours and pretend to eat grass. However, something had to be done!

This was when Diana Slack, a neighbour from Raisbeck, suggested that her old mare, who had not got a foal, but who was kind and gentle would take Annie under her 'wing' through the day and Diana would feed her goat's milk morning and night. This plan worked. Diana bought Annie, and Diana's mare taught Annie to eat grass.

I resisted the temptation to visit (in case I upset things) until the following spring when Annie was a yearling. I walked into the field where she was grazing with a companion and facing away from me. I gave the call that I had always given her as a foal and she immediately lifted her head, turned around and galloped down the field to me. There was never any doubt in my mind that she remembered me and my voice and the call. I did not see her for another two years during which time she was away from Raisbeck. One evening Diana telephoned and invited me to go to her house for a glass of wine and very mysteriously she said that she had someone I might like to meet.

As soon as I got out of the car, I spotted Annie in the front paddock; by now a well developed three-year-old. I gave the old call and it is just as well there was a fence between us as otherwise I would have been knocked over as Annie responded at a gallop to her 'Mother's' call once again. Annie's registered name is Lunesdale Black Beauty and I am not sure where she is now other than in my heart and memory.

Another story, which proved to me that these ponies also have excellent memory of places, was a rather sadder one than that of Annie. We sold a very good yearling filly that had been bred and lived on the fell. I shall not go into details, save to say that she had no freedom in her new home and was confined to a box full time. Stories that I was hearing about her worried me greatly and after two years I heard that she was for sale. I bought her back and went to collect her.

She was in great physical shape but sadly in poor mental health. A friend and I went to collect her and she never moved in the horsebox on the way home. When I unloaded her in our yard, she immediately turned round, lifted her head and gazed up towards the fell; the place where she was reared. She stayed in this position, trembling from head to foot for a long time and I did not try to lead her into a box until she signalled that she was ready and stopped trembling. She had come home; to my mind she recognised and remembered those hills without any doubt. I spent many hours with her and slowly, over the next few months, her confidence and mental health returned, and I showed her successfully, before putting her in foal and returning her to her birthplace where she has spent many happy years and rewarded us with some lovely foals.

Yet another example of memory was started on the day that Lunesdale Rebecca foaled for the first time. I have already explained that her mother, Lunesdale White Rose, was patrolling back and forth between Rebecca and the other mares, looking extremely belligerent and perhaps sensing that all was not well. When we arrived on the scene, Rebecca was looking bewildered and the filly foal was wandering about and obviously had not suckled. When we looked closely at Rebecca we could see why - she appeared to have absolutely no udder! I started off back to the farm with one arm around the foal who very obligingly latched itself on to me and was happy to accompany me!

Rebecca did not follow and was extremely upset and Bert decided to go back to the farm for a halter with which to lead her down. After about half an hour we had both the foal and Rebecca in a loose box next to the house and within ten minutes Rebecca started to relax and we could scarcely believe our eyes! Her so far nonexistent udder started to swell like a balloon and milk dripped from it! We pushed the foal under her and it started to suckle. We decided to keep them in the paddock at the back of the house for a few days to keep an eye on them. The foal however, which we named Lady Rebecca, seemed to have a problem deciding whether Rebecca (who supplied the milk) or myself (who she had identified with shortly after her birth) was her mother!

This resulted in the foal galloping between myself and Rebecca every time I hung out the washing or went into the back paddock for any other reason! Obviously this state of affairs could not be allowed to continue, so Rebecca and daughter were sent back to the herd. I however, could not resist going to visit them more often than I should have, and delighted in the fact that this foal would leave the herd, and often bring along another foal to 'meet' me!

This situation has continued for six years and I could always count on Lady Rebecca leaving the herd and coming to me until the spring of 2006 when she gave birth to her first foal! The 'wild' instinct kicked in, which was obviously stronger than that of memory and trust of humans, and although she did not run from me she would not allow me to approach near enough to touch her and would keep herself between her foal and me! This state of affairs carried on for a month or so until she satisfied herself that I was not a threat and we have since resumed our earlier special friendship. I have an even greater respect for the wild instinct that puts her protection of her foal above all else, including her friendship with me!

WEATHER

THERE ARE CERTAIN times of the year when the ponies can be found on different areas of the fell. They tend to stick to the higher parts in the summer where it is cooler, breezier and they are less likely to be bothered by flies. This is also better for the foals as very hot conditions can lead to the foals sleeping for too long and not suckling frequently enough, which can lead to either dehydration or 'scouring.' They will also be nearer to a stream in hotter and drier weather when not as much moisture is available from the grass.

As Roundthwaite Common is a series of hills and valleys, they also know where the best places are to shelter from wind, rain and snow. They have also learned that hay will be available at the point nearest to the farm and will arrive there before a snowstorm. This, without exception, takes place twenty four hours before the snow arrives and these ponies are never wrong! How they sense the coming of snow, I have yet to learn. We know that ponies are capable of hearing sounds that are indistinguishable to the human ear so maybe they can also smell things that we cannot. Maybe they can 'smell' the coming of snow or maybe there is a change

Ponies will flee from the direction and therefore, the perceived danger of, an electrical storm.

in the atmosphere that is tangible to them but not to us humans.

In heavy rain they will stop eating, turn their backs to the direction that the wind is coming from, hunch their backs up and lower their heads and tails. If the rainfall is light the ponies will continue to graze without being perturbed. They dislike strong winds and will again put their backs towards it and adopt a miserable expression. It is said that the shape of the equine ear 'distorts' sounds and therefore strong wind 'spooks' the ponies. It is certainly noticeable that wild ponies are unhappy in strong winds and domesticated ponies can also react in quite unexpected ways on windy days.

Equally, like many humans, they are nervous of storms, especially electrical ones. The tension is especially obvious in their hindquarters, when the muscles will be more obvious and they will snort and kick, lifting their heads and tails and moving their ears in all directions. The leader will often see a storm as a situation of alarm and may give the signal to run in the direction where the storm looks to be the least dangerous.

There are weather conditions that they love; gentle breezes will initiate playing and gambolling especially amongst the youngsters. Clear sunny days of winter will

Feeding wild ponies in winter is like feeding the wild birds in your garden. It does not make them any less wild, it merely makes life easier for them.

make them alert and they will sometimes enjoy a roll in the cold, soft snow. Whilst we provide hay for them when the snow comes, and they return to the fell gate near the farm, they are quite adept at digging away the snow with their front feet to reveal the grass underneath.

Nature provides these wild Fell ponies with the best equipment possible for the bad weather: their thick coats full of natural oils, full manes and tails giving maximum protection. Equally in hot weather, the abundant tails make effective fly swatters and long forelocks keep the flies from their eyes.

Domesticated ponies take full advantage of any trees in hot weather both for providing shade and for ridding their faces of flies by poking them in amongst the leaves. There are no trees available on the highest parts of the fells, and the few flies that venture to these heights are not able to be brushed off with leaves. The wild ponies compensate by allowing each other to brush them off by means of sticking their heads under the tails of friendly companion ponies.

Social Behaviour of Youngsters

WHEN A FOAL is born into the herd, its first weeks of life are spent suckling, sleeping, exploring the environment and playing under the watchful and affectionate eye of its mother. During these first few weeks, when the foal sleeps, the mare will stop grazing and stand guard over it, continually on the alert for danger. The natural curiosity of the foal will lead it to approach strange objects and leave its mother in order to play with other foals within the group.

The mechanism of recognition between a mare and foal is one in which the sense of smell plays a major part in that the mare touches the foal's body with her muzzle before allowing it to suck. She will not normally allow a foal other than her own to suckle and it will get sharply chased away. There are exceptions, and whilst we have not experienced them, we have heard of barren mares 'stealing' the new born foals of other mares. This happens regularly within the sheep flock and causes many problems at lambing time!

In the wild, if left to its own devices, a foal would suckle its mother almost up until another sibling was born. During these first months of life, the foals learn that not all of the herd members are equal! It is a time to learn respect and adopt an attitude of submission before an older or larger animal.

It is a time to learn how to approach another foal and how to indulge in mutual grooming sessions. It is a time to learn that orders must be obeyed without question, especially orders to run, as safety may be at stake.

It is a time for fun and playing and play fighting. It is a time for exploring the surroundings and foals have an insatiable curiosity. Like human babies most of the new things that they encounter are first 'explored' by mouth. We decided to take Lunesdale Rebecca to the Fell Pony Society Breed Show at Penrith with her first foal (Lady Rebecca) at foot.

The afternoon before the show I undertook to shampoo Rebecca and prepare her for the show. It was a very hot sunny day and I set buckets of hot and cold water out in the yard, plus shampoo, conditioner for mane and tail and brushes, combs, etc. I then tied Rebecca to the wall, rolled up my sleeves and started to wash her. The process was frequently interrupted by her foal, Lady Rebecca, who when she was not tipping over buckets of water or picking up shampoo bottles was having to be extricated from the tack room or trying to enter into mutual grooming sessions with myself. I remember that it was a very hot day and extremely stressful!

I eventually got Rebecca looking clean and smart and the next day we set off to the show. We went into the mare and foal class and Lady Rebecca was unusually naughty; aiming kicks at her mother and wearing a very sulky face. On leaving the ring we were stood chatting to a few people who were admiring Rebecca, when a friend said, "Excuse me Carole, but there appears to be part of a rubber glove sticking out of that foal's bottom!"

I lifted the tail of Lady Rebecca and sure enough there was a finger of a rubber glove showing! I pulled this and a whole rubber glove shot out! One of the wittier members of our family said, "Well there is his glove, now where is the vet?"

For my part I was both amazed and relieved that this could have passed through a foal's digestive system without killing it! Obviously the foal had encountered this curious object whilst I was washing her mother and had swallowed it. This accounted for her naughty behaviour in the ring; she was obviously suffering some pain whilst the glove was 'passing through'! Never underestimate the curiosity of Fell pony foals!

At the end of the first year the foals learn to emit a 'frightened' whinny when they feel intimidated. At the age of two, this foal whinny disappears; a sign that although it is a weaker member of the herd, it should now be treated like an adult. Also at the age of two, the fillies tend to refrain from rearing up and play fighting each other, although the colts continue to do this play fighting for longer.

By this time, within the Lunesdale herd, the fillies are back in their family groups and the colts which are to be kept as future stallions, are in a bachelor group and are establishing their own hierarchy.

Gathering

BEING THE 'GUARDIANS' of semi-feral ponies has its pleasures and they are plentiful. To be able to go up the fell on a peaceful summer's evening and watch, from a respectable distance, the foals playing, the mares grazing or grooming each other in such spectacular scenery is an almost indescribable pleasure and privilege. Taking hay up on a winter's day, with snow on the ground and a wind that freezes your face and takes your breath away is not quite so pleasant, but nevertheless is a task that has to be done.

Perhaps the use of the term 'semi-feral' should be explained. The word 'feral' means wild and thus the term semi-feral means semi-wild. This actually means that the ponies are left as much as possible to enjoy the freedom of running wild and thus retain their natural instincts, whilst also being 'protected' to a certain extent.

One only has to watch a wildlife programme on the television to understand that nature can be cruel. Some animals are hunters and some animals sadly are the prey of these hunters. Frequently, in the true wild, only the fittest and strongest of a species will survive. However, with animals that are actually owned by someone, it would not be acceptable in today's society to let these animals die in harsh winter conditions just because there

is no grass available for perhaps weeks on end. In my opinion, feeding them hay when the weather is harsh is no different to putting food out for the wild birds in the garden. It does not make them any less wild; it just makes their lives a little easier!

Neither would it be acceptable to let the mares give birth unsupervised and perhaps die because a foal was coming backwards, or had a leg stuck back or because the mare had retained the afterbirth and infection had set in. Also, in maiden mares (giving birth for the first time) they are sometimes tender or 'ticklish' in the udder area and will refuse to allow the foal to suckle. It is of the greatest importance that a foal gets the colostrum or 'first milk' in the hours immediately after birth. This colostrum gives it immunity from certain illnesses until it has built up its own immune system. Having the mares near to the farm therefore at foaling time enables us to keep an eye on the situation and avoid unnecessary losses.

We also attempt to spray the navel of each foal with strong iodine as soon as possible after birth as the open end of the navel 'cord' can be a means by which infection can enter the foal's body. This is possibly not as necessary when mares foal on 'clean' land, but as ours foal on land where previously sheep have lambed, we

feel that is necessary to take this precaution. This really does need to be done as soon as possible after birth, otherwise the foals are too quick and strong to restrain! The mares are also quite belligerent and it is a two man job; one to hold and spray the foal's navel and one to keep the mare at bay with a stout walking stick whilst this is carried out! Over the years we have almost perfected a system whereby we drive the mare and foal into the corner of a particular field that has a gate in this corner. One of us opens the gate and if you are really quick you can let the mare through whilst keeping the foal at the other side where it can be quickly upturned, the navel sprayed and the foal returned to its dam within a minute.

So, living a semi-feral existence means that these ponies have the best of both worlds. They live the major part of the year on the fells, as nature intended but also receive guardianship. This means that they are gathered and brought home before the mares are due to foal and at other times to be wormed. All of them therefore have been haltered at some time or another – usually when foals or yearlings. This does not mean that they are tame and will be caught easily or will even be co-operative once caught. Far from it!

The gathering nowadays is done by means of a quad bike and the family groups are all herded together and brought down to the farm. This is when the 'hierarchy' system can be plainly seen and the older 'leaders' are always in front, with the subordinates in their rightful places, but in the absence of a stallion, the quad bike brings up the rear!

Once the ponies are home and in the yard, they are driven individually into a handily situated loose box where, once cornered, they can be wormed. Following the early May gather, the mares are left to foal in the 'in fields' and providing the foaling is trouble free they are left alone, and after the foal's navel has been treated with antiseptic they are returned to the fell, together with their foals, as soon as is practicable.

Other semi-feral Native British ponies are also subject to being gathered at certain times of the year. In the case of the ponies of the New Forest, where ponies belonging to several different owners run in the same area, they are gathered in order for the foals to be identified with the owner's mark.

Continued interference (by those who do not understand) and the ever increasing demand for 'paperwork' is making the guardianship of native breeds of semi-feral ponies more and more difficult. The demands of identification, passports, and microchips mean considerably more expense and more handling of the ponies. Coupled with the continuing pressure to remove grazing animals of all kinds from the Cumbrian fells, there is less and less incentive for future generations to continue to maintain these semi-feral herds.

In order to try to raise awareness of this, we held an open day at the Lunesdale Stud in July 2000. Part of the day consisted of gathering the ponies and driving them down from Roundthwaite Common for approximately 130 spectators to witness.

Along with a display of photographs we placed the following words:

We hope that those of you here today will have enjoyed the sight of these semi-feral ponies coming down from the fell, (a sight that will perhaps be denied to our grandchildren). We also hope that you will acknowledge that being the guardians of such a herd is at times a difficult and time consuming job. We hope that you will join with us in trying to spread the word that these ponies are a major part of our Cumbrian heritage, which seems to be constantly under threat from those who do not know or understand our way of life.

This open day took a lot of work, time and planning. Just to be sure that all the ponies came down from the fell in one big herd at a set time was a major planning exercise in itself! Two days were spent tracking down the family groups and noting the whereabouts of all of the ponies. On the morning of the open day, a friend set off on a quad bike at dawn and gathered them all up and kept them in a large herd out of sight of the farm. Thanks to mobile phones we were able to bring them down from the fell 'on cue'!

The exercise was worthwhile, however, as not just the people in attendance on the day, but others who read about it and saw pictures in equine magazines, were made aware of the existence of these semi-feral Fell ponies and the need to keep them here.

These are some extracts from letters received after the event:

"Thank you for allowing us the privilege to see this herd of ponies. It is an experience many of us will not forget." *B & R Dunne, Barnard Castle.*

"The sight of your 'drive' off the fell was one that will always remain a highlight in my memory." *Jean Ward, Lamplugh.*

"I will never forget the sight of the mares, foals and yearlings coming down from the fell. A truly fantastic sight." *Bill Watts, Racehorse Trainer. Richmond.*

"The memory of seeing the mares and foals coming over the brow of the hill will be one that we will both treasure." *Mr and Mrs Stockburn, Harrogate.*

"The sight of those ponies coming off the fell will remain in my memory for a long time." *Stella Peters-Preston.*

From *Scottish Equestrian* magazine, October 2000:

"Earlier this summer, Carole and Bert Morland, owners of one of the few remaining herds of semi-feral Fell ponies held an open day at their Lunesdale stud in Cumbria. What a day that was for those of us lucky enough to be invited!

"Undoubtedly, the greatest thrill was to see the Lunesdale herd of mares and foals being rounded up by

The Gather. Photograph courtesy of Kit Houghton.

a man on a quad bike and brought down from the fell to the farm. Our first glimpse, as we watched from the bottom of the fell, was of the ponies streaming across the brow of the hill above us, before disappearing behind a ridge. A short time later they reappeared on the skyline. Then slowly at first they moved down the fell towards us, gathering speed as they came, until they were galloping effortlessly over the steep rough ground, manes and tails flowing, before slowing down to trot along the road and into the farm field.

"It was an unforgettable sight. But as Carole pointed out, it was a sight that may be denied to future generations, as it is a difficult, expensive and time consuming job being the guardians of such a herd. She expressed the hope that those present would join her and Bert in helping to make people who do not understand this, realise that the only way that these hill herds can survive in these difficult times, is if everything is made as simple as possible with no unnecessary handling of the ponies and no unnecessary expense."

Characteristics and why the Fell ponies and the Cumbrian hills need each other

THE FELL PONY SOCIETY has a breed standard that describes the 'perfect' Fell pony and to which all breeders should aspire. The points described in this breed standard were originally based on these true 'Hill ponies' and are not merely for 'cosmetic' purposes. They are the points that both enable a Fell pony to survive in a feral herd on these Northern hills and also when domesticated, enable them to work effectively.

There is no doubt that some of these characteristic points will be lost if Fell ponies are only bred on lowland farms in the future. There is nothing wrong with breeding Fell ponies in environments other than their native hills, but it is my opinion that unless lowland breeders are able to return to a 'fell bred' stallion every few generations, the animals will become larger and breed type will be lost.

On the other hand the hills themselves need the ponies along with the sheep to continue to graze them, otherwise the countryside as all of us (tourists and locals alike) know and enjoy it at the moment will be lost. The grazing habits of the sheep and ponies compliment each other and help to keep scrub and undesirable weeds at bay and make it possible for the fells to be walked and enjoyed. Other species live in harmony with the ponies and many a bird's nest is woven or lined with horsehair.

Since the Fell pony breed evolved, these ponies have been famous for their versatility. Their strength and stamina is legendary which made carrying loads, pulling farm machinery, shepherding and trotting for long distances no problem to them. This strength, stamina and agility on the most difficult of terrain, has evolved through living on the high Northern fells.

The small ears and large nostrils demanded by the Fell Pony Society breed standard are not merely to make them look pretty! Small ears can be protected in winter weather by their heavy and abundant manes and so will not suffer from frostbite. Large 'square' nostrils will ensure maximum oxygen intake, which is necessary when climbing steep slopes. The traditional 'moustache' and under chin whiskers are an extra sensory organ and will tell the wild Fell pony much about the vegetation that these hairs encounter before the pony eats it.

The profuse mane and tail, which should not be trimmed in showing classes, is invaluable as protection against the elements on the high fells as is the thick coat containing natural oils.

Lunesdale Evening Star being driven by 74-year-old Bert Morland at Lowther, 2007.

Stennerskeugh Joanne wins at a show in Belgium.

Bert Morland judges a Fell stallion in Pennsylvania, USA.

Strong thighs and second thighs are also indispensable when climbing steep slopes. Sloping pasterns help to absorb shock when traversing rough and sometimes stony ground and good round hard hooves are essential.

The 'all round' action of a Fell pony, greatly admired in the show ring or in a driving pony, is necessary on these rugged hills. A pony with a 'daisy cutting' action would soon come to grief on this rough ground.

The maximum height of a registered Fell pony used to be 13.2h.h. but has in recent years been increased to 14h.h. This increase may be acceptable for Fell ponies bred and reared in lowland environments but ponies of the traditional height of 13.2h.h. and under are the only ones able to maintain condition on the open fells in winter.

A frequently misunderstood part of the breed standard is that regarding the 'feather' which is the long silky hair around the pony's feet. The breed standard states that, "this may be cast in summer except that at point of heel." Many people think that this means that all the feather may be cast in summer but it actually means that only the long hair from the back of the knees may be cast. The hair at the heel and around the front of the hoof (the spat) should be retained.

Grey stallion, Lunesdale Mountain Mist, wows the crowds at Pardubice in the Czech Republic.

This protective feather is not cast as much by 'true' hill bred ponies as it is much cooler on the top of the fells where they tend to spend the summer months as they are less bothered by flies here. It is more frequently cast by ponies kept in lowland situations and when the weather is especially hot and the 'feather' is invaded by mites which can cause a condition known as 'grease', Fell ponies have been observed to bite off their own feather when suffering from this condition.

The breed standard also says that the Fell pony should have the, "unmistakable appearance of hardiness peculiar to the mountain pony." This really means that the ponies should have flat, flinty bone, appear tough enough to withstand the elements and be muscular rather than fat. Although the breed standard claims that it is 'unmistakable' there are nevertheless quite a few judges who fail to recognise it given the number of round boned, soft and over weight ponies that are frequently given preference in the show ring over those with this supposedly 'unmistakable' hardiness.

The hill ponies do not get overweight as even during the times of year when the grass is plentiful, they are constantly on the move and climbing the steep slopes. They therefore have considerably less trouble both getting pregnant and giving birth than their domesticated and usually fatter counterparts, and we have never encountered a case of laminitis in a semi-feral pony.

These wild Fell ponies are extremely intelligent and could even be said to be 'crafty'. Capturing them on such a vast acreage as the fells can be difficult if they do not want to be caught; with them knowing only too well the places that are too difficult to access with a quad bike. Before the invention of the quad bike, our ponies had to be gathered on horse back. This was on occasions a very difficult task and it was made easier by threading a plastic feed sack through the collar of a sheep dog and sending this sheep dog around the herd. The wild ponies were not afraid of a dog, but were very afraid of a seemingly 'moving' large piece of plastic or hemp! However, this intelligence is partly what enables them to survive so well as a semi-feral herd and to teach their young these ways of survival. It is also part of their charm and what makes them, when domesticated, able to cope extremely well with whatever man asks of them.

FINALLY...

IT HAS BEEN my privilege to watch and learn from these beautiful wild ponies, living as nature intended them to live. I hope that by recording my observations of them, others may also learn something that will help them to communicate better with their own Fell pony. Most of all, I hope it will inspire the people of Cumbria to cherish these ponies as part of their natural heritage.

When people mention Dartmoor, Exmoor, the New Forest or the Shetland Isles they immediately associate these areas with ponies of the same name. For some reason that association has not happened to the same extent with the Cumbrian 'fells' and Fell ponies, although wild Fell ponies have run on these hills for generations.

I shall remember for the rest of my days being invited to a 'drift' in the New Forest. This is an occasion when local 'Foresters' mounted on their own New Forest ponies, come together to round up the wild forest ponies to brand them. Not only was it a spectacular

The Fell pony is the all-round family pony as demonstrated by grey Lunesdale Storm Cloud, being ridden by Julie Robinson (next page) and her eleven-year-old daughter Alex at Fell Pony Society shows in 2006. Photographs courtesy of Ken Etteridge.

event, but one which showed the tremendous pride that the people living in and around the New Forest in Hampshire have in their native breed of pony.

I hope that in time, with proper education and publicity, the people of Cumbria will become as fiercely proud of their native breed of pony as the New Forest people are of theirs. They are indeed something to be proud of!

Their versatility is incredible and some ponies bred on these Cumbrian fells are not only competing, but also succeeding in many different disciplines world wide. Their toughness, intelligence and kind nature has resulted in increasing demand and popularity and there are now Fell ponies in Ireland, the Channel Islands, France, Belgium, Germany, Holland, Switzerland, Spain, Denmark, the Czech Republic, Australia, Canada and America. Her Majesty the Queen breeds them and Prince Philip has for many years competed at Lowther driving trials with a team of four Fell ponies.

I hope that the Fell pony will in the future be recognised as being as much a part of Cumbria's heritage as the lakes, the mountains, the stone walls, John Peel, the farming and the rare breeds of sheep.

My final wish and one of the reasons for writing this book is, that after mine and my husband's day, future generations will take an interest and Fell ponies will continue to live and breed on the hills of Cumbria. These ponies are proud and noble creatures. They have served us very well. They have gone to war on our

behalf, they have been mainstays in the agricultural and mining industries. They have been and continue to be the ultimate family pony.

They are beautiful and they belong here on the hills of Cumbria......

FELL PONIES have been bred at the Lunesdale Fell Pony Stud for more than 50 years. Bert Morland has farmed at Roundthwaite, near Tebay, for over forty years, during which time he has kept and bred Fell ponies. He is interested in every aspect of the Fell pony and has spent many hours watching the herd in their natural habitat. He has been a Fell pony and M & M Judge since he was in his twenties. He no longer rides but still drives a Fell pony occasionally.

Carole Morland has also had a life long interest in Fell ponies and still occasionally hacks out. She is also a Judge of Fell and M & M ponies and together with Bert still shows in hand at both local and national levels.

To find out more see:

www.lunesdalestud.com